FOLLOW ME

Meeting Jesus in the Gospel of John

EDWARD SRI

ASCENSION

West Chester, Pennsylvania

Nihil obstat: Rev. Robert A. Pesarchick, S.T.L., S.T.D.
           Censor librorum
           June 9, 2016

Imprimatur: +Most Reverend Charles J. Chaput, O.F.M. Cap.
           Archbishop of Philadelphia
           June 24, 2016

Ascension
Post Office Box 1990
West Chester, PA 19380
1-800-376-0520
ascensionpress.com

Cover design: Devin Schadt
Cover art: *Christ and the Woman of Samaria at the Well,* by Guercino

Printed in the United States of America
ISBN 978-1-945179-00-6

FOLLOW ME

Meeting Jesus in the Gospel of John

Saint Brigid Catholic Church

All Souls Day Novena of Masses

for the
Commemoration of
the Faithful Departed,
November 2nd – 10th.
In the Holy Sacrifice of the
Mass, please remember our
deceased loved ones:

1. _____

2. _____

3. _____

4. _____

5. _____

My Name: _____

My Address: _____

My Offering:

*May eternal rest grant them O Lord, and let perpetual
light shine upon them. May they rest in peace.*

About *Follow Me: Meeting Jesus in the Gospel of John*

The Gospel of John is unique. The Synoptic Gospels (Matthew, Mark, and Luke) are similar to each other in many respects, but readers of John's Gospel will notice that his is remarkably different. Many of the events he writes about are not found in the Synoptic Gospels, and many of the events found in the Synoptic Gospels are not found in John's Gospel. John seems to acknowledge this difference when he writes, "Jesus did many other signs in the presence of the disciples, which are not written in this book; but these are written that you may believe that Jesus is the Christ, the Son of God, and that believing you may have life in his name" (John 20:30-31). This passage reveals the purpose of John's Gospel, which is also the purpose of this study.

Follow Me: Meeting Jesus in the Gospel of John will guide you through John's Gospel and invite you to encounter Christ every step of the way. As you read about Jesus calling his first disciples, meeting the woman at the well, and offering himself for us on the Cross, you are invited to enter these dramatic moments, not as a bystander, but as a witness of God's merciful love for us made manifest in Jesus Christ.

Materials Needed for the Study

- **Workbook** *(needed by every participant):* This includes session overviews, talk notes for the video presentations, discussion questions, closing prayers, and home preparation readings for each session.

- **Leader's Guide** *(needed by every leader and facilitator):* This Leader's Guide includes everything that is in the participant Workbook. Additionally, it includes instructions for leaders and small-group facilitators, as well as responses to the discussion questions.

- **Video Presentations** *(for everyone to view):* In these videos, Dr. Edward Sri presents an intriguing overview and explanation of the Gospel of John, while providing unique insights that will help you to have a powerful encounter with Christ in Scripture.

In addition to these materials, every participant, leader, and small-group facilitator should have a Catholic Bible. We recommend *The Great Adventure Catholic Bible.* It is also recommended that leaders and facilitators have the *Catechism of the Catholic Church.*

How the Study Works

Each session of *Follow Me* includes the four steps shown in the graphic below. The first three steps take place when a group meets each week. The fourth step, Home Preparation, is completed by participants on their own in preparation for the next session. A brief description of each step is given in the Session One "Opening Review" on page 3.

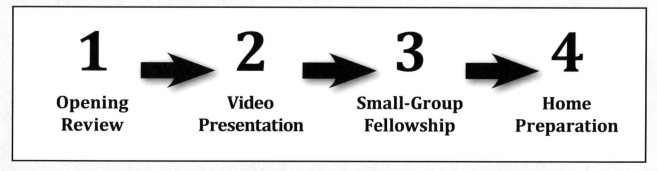

1	2	3	4
Opening Review	**Video Presentation**	**Small-Group Fellowship**	**Home Preparation**

Getting the Most Out of this Study

This study will help you come to know Christ and the Gospel of John in a new way. The riches of John's Gospel and of the entire Bible are inexhaustible, so in some sense, Scripture will always remain a mystery, but that is part of the beauty of it. The Bible is not a subject to master; it is a place where we can experience an encounter with God.

Whenever you open your Bible to read, *start with a prayer*, and place yourself in God's presence. You might take Samuel's prayer as your own: "Speak, [LORD], for your servant is listening" (1 Samuel 3:10, NAB). When you read, take a moment to listen. Try not to treat Scripture as a text, but as a personal message from God. What is he saying? What does it mean? What does it mean for your life? If you come to the Word focused on having an encounter with God, he will speak to your heart, and you will be transformed by it.

Ten Commandments of Small-Group Discussion[1]

1. Enjoy yourself!

2. Speak with respect and charity.

3. Do not ridicule or dismiss what others say. Keep comments positive.

4. Come prepared.

5. If you were not able to prepare, let others speak first.

6. Stick to the topic and questions at hand.

7. Start and end on time.

8. Allow silence. Give people a chance to think.

9. Listen to others without interrupting.

10. Keep personal matters within the group.

---

[1] Adapted from Thomas Smith's original "10 Commandments of a Small Group."

Session Outline

There are eight sessions in *Follow Me: Meeting Jesus in the Gospel of John*. In addition to a video presentation for each of these sessions, there is also an introductory video about the study and how it works.

Session (Video Times)	Title	Gospel Readings
Introductory Video (2:18)	About *Follow Me: Meeting Jesus in the Gospel of John*	—
Session One (32:12)	"In the Beginning": Jesus at the Center	John 1:1–18
Session Two (33:46)	"Come and See": Becoming Disciples	John 1:19–2:25
Session Three (31:57)	At the Well: Our Deepest Thirst	John 3:1–4:42
Session Four (34:27)	"Believe in Me": Trust and Surrender	John 4:43–6:71
Session Five (33:00)	Encountering Mercy	John 7–9
Session Six (32:52)	The Law of Self-Giving	John 10–12
Session Seven (29:56)	The New Commandment and Life in the Spirit	John 13–17
Session Eight (35:30)	"It Is Finished": A Dying and Rising Love	John 18–21

Frequently Asked Questions

1. Which Bible should I use?

For this study, you will want to use a Catholic edition of the Bible. We recommend *The Great Adventure Catholic Bible.*

2. How do I find a Scripture reference in my Bible?

Each book of the Bible is divided into chapters, and each chapter is made up of a series of numbered verses. To aid readers in finding a particular biblical verse, each Scripture passage has an "address," a location reference made up of the name of the book, followed by the chapter and verse numbers.

For example:

- 1 Samuel 7 refers to the entire seventh chapter of the book of 1 Samuel (pronounced "first Samuel" because there also is a 2 Samuel, or "second Samuel").
- Genesis 1:1 refers to the book of Genesis, Chapter 1, verse 1.
- Numbers 5:2-6 refers to the book of Numbers, Chapter 5, verses 2 through 6.
- 1 Corinthians 3:2-6, 7-10 refers to the book of 1 Corinthians ("first Corinthians"), Chapter 3, verses 2 through 6 and verses 7 through 10.

Abbreviations are often used in Scripture references. For example, "Jn 3:16" means "John, Chapter 3, verse 16." A list of abbreviations is found in the front of your Bible. To locate a particular book, use your Bible's contents page. As a general rule, Ascension Bible studies do not use Bible book abbreviations.

3. What is the Bible?

The Bible is the written expression of the Word of God. Although it contains seventy-three books written over many centuries by many different human authors in several languages, the Bible is also a unified whole because all its books are inspired by the Holy Spirit, and, together, they reveal God's plan of salvation.

Because God inspired the Bible's human authors, he is the principal Author of Scripture. As such, the Bible is inerrant ("without error"). As the Second Vatican Council's document on Sacred Scripture, *Dei Verbum* ("Word of God"), states:

> Therefore, since everything asserted by the inspired authors or sacred writers must be held to be asserted by the Holy Spirit, it follows that the books of Scripture must be acknowledged as teaching solidly, faithfully and without error that truth which God wanted put into sacred writings for the sake of salvation.[2]

4. What are the Old and New Testaments?

The books of the Bible are grouped under two headings—the Old Testament and the New Testament. The word "testament" can also be translated "covenant," which clarifies the meaning of these titles. The Old Testament tells how God made a series of covenants (i.e., binding agreements) with his people Israel in which he promised blessing in return for loving obedience. The New Testament tells how God fulfilled this promise of blessing by means of a new and everlasting covenant in his Son, Jesus Christ.

5. Why are Catholic and Protestant Bibles different?

Both Catholic and Protestant versions of the Bible contain the same twenty-seven books of the New Testament. It is the Old Testament that differs. The books of the New Testament are arranged in the following order:

- Four Gospels (Matthew, Mark, Luke, and John) and the Acts of the Apostles
- St. Paul's letters (or "epistles") to the early Christian churches – Romans; 1 and 2 Corinthians; Galatians; Ephesians; Philippians; Colossians; 1 and 2 Thessalonians
- "Pastoral letters" – 1 and 2 Timothy; Titus; Philemon; Hebrews
- "Catholic letters" (James; 1 and 2 Peter; 1, 2, and 3 John; Jude) and the book of Revelation

---

[2] *Dei Verbum* (DV) 11. For more on canonicity, inspiration, and inerrancy, see the resources listed on page ix.

In the early days of the Church, two versions of the Old Testament were used by the Jewish people. One, written entirely in Hebrew, contained thirty-nine books. The other, a Greek translation known as the Septuagint, contained forty-six books—the same thirty-nine as the Hebrew version plus another seven.

In AD 393, the bishops of the Church, with the authority given them by Christ, determined the list of inspired books of Scripture. This list contained the forty-six books of the Septuagint, which had been used by Christians since the first century. So, the Old Testament of the Church had forty-six books for more than a thousand years.

During the Protestant Reformation in the sixteenth century, the reformers chose to follow the shorter Hebrew collection of thirty-nine books. At the Council of Trent in 1546, the Septuagint's list of forty-six books was declared by the Catholic Church to be the "canon" (or "authoritative list of inspired books") of Scripture.

Here are the books of the Old Testament as found in Catholic versions of the Bible, listed by type of literature. The seven "deuterocanonical" books (which Protestants refer to as the "apocryphal books" or "the Apocrypha") are listed in italics:

- Pentateuch – Genesis; Exodus; Leviticus; Numbers; Deuteronomy
- Historical books – Joshua; Judges; Ruth; 1 and 2 Samuel; 1 and 2 Kings; 1 and 2 Chronicles; Ezra; Nehemiah; *Tobit; Judith;* Esther; and *1 and 2 Maccabees*
- Wisdom books – Job; Psalms; Proverbs; Ecclesiastes; Song of Solomon (Song of Songs); *Wisdom of Solomon; Sirach*
- Prophets – Isaiah; Jeremiah; Lamentations; *Baruch;* Ezekiel; Daniel; Hosea; Joel; Amos; Obadiah; Jonah; Micah; Nahum; Habakkuk; Zephaniah; Haggai; Zechariah; Malachi

Some deuterocanonical portions of Esther and Daniel are not included in Protestant versions.

6. What are the notes that appear in some Bibles?

The explanatory notes that appear in many versions of the Bible reflect the theological stance of their editors and the scholarship at the time of publication. All notes published in Catholic Bibles have received the Imprimatur of a bishop, which is an official permission to publish that carries with it the assurance that nothing in the book is contrary to the faith or morality of the Church. (An Imprimatur does not imply that the bishop who granted it agrees with the notes' content or that they are official Church teaching, however.) The notes are not considered part of Sacred Scripture and, therefore, are not divinely inspired.

7. Where can I find answers to my other questions about the Bible?

We recommend the following books and resources:

- *The Catechism of the Catholic Church.* For information about Sacred Scripture, its relationship to Sacred Tradition, and its inspiration and interpretation, see paragraphs 50 through 141. (The *Catechism* is available online and in published editions.)
- *Catholic Bible Dictionary,* Scott Hahn, general editor
- *The Bible Compass: A Catholic's Guide to Navigating the Scriptures,* by Edward Sri
- *Praying Scripture for a Change: An Introduction to Lectio Divina,* by Tim Gray
- *Walking with God: A Journey Through the Bible,* by Tim Gray and Jeff Cavins

The Holy Trinity, by Caro

Session One

"In the Beginning": Jesus at the Center

John 1:1-18

Session Overview

Holy Trinity, by Theodoor van Thulden

Religion is often described as man's search for God. But Christianity is much more about God's search for us. We see this especially in the opening passages of John's Gospel, which reveal that God is madly in love with us—he pursues us and wants a relationship with us and wants to forgive us, comfort us, heal us, and guide us to true happiness. Even though we turned away from him in many ways, his love for us drove him to become one of us—he "became flesh and dwelt among us" (John 1:14)—in Jesus Christ in order to die for our sins and draw us back to himself.

Many people today do not know about God's amazing love. They view God as either a harsh judge, who will not forgive them of their sins, or as impersonal—distant, uninvolved, and indifferent about their lives. Or they make God in their own image—conveniently approving their way of thinking and living and never challenging them to change.

A journey through John's Gospel, however, will challenge all of us to encounter God anew in Jesus Christ. As we will see, Jesus is not just a moral teacher or spiritual guide, but the God who became Man. And that sets him apart from all other religious leaders in the world's history. When we see Jesus, we see the face of God. Indeed, in Jesus Christ, the God of love has unveiled himself most fully to the human family. And he is inviting us to an intimate relationship with him. Some people keep Jesus at a distance as just a part of their lives. But he wants to be at the very center of our lives. Will you let him in?

Step 1: Opening Review (5 minutes)

Use this time during the first session to get to know the others in your group and to familiarize yourself with this workbook, the "Ten Commandments of Small-Group Discussion" found on page vi, and the following four steps that you will follow for each session.

Step 1: Opening Review (5 minutes) – One or more questions will be presented at the beginning of each session to help you recall the main theme from the previous session and to help you prepare for what you will cover next.

Step 2: Video Presentation (30-35 minutes) – The *Follow Me* video presentations will guide you through the Gospel of John, providing unique insights and focusing on practical themes we can apply to our lives—themes such as discipleship, humility, mercy, and love.

Step 3: Small-Group Fellowship (30-40 minutes) – Engaging discussion questions will give you and your group an opportunity to grow in fellowship as you explore the profound mysteries of the Gospel of John. Each session will close with a prayer that relates to that week's theme.

Step 4: Home Preparation: Looking Ahead – To prepare for the next session, you will be asked to read passages from the Gospel of John and to ponder some of the points from your reading.

The Seven Signs

The word "sign" is used often in the New Testament to describe Jesus' mighty deeds. In the Gospel of John, however, these signs are more than displays of Jesus' divine power. They each unveil something important about his identity and mission. The seven signs in John's Gospel are:

1. The changing of water to wine at Cana (see 2:1-11)
2. The healing of the royal official's son (see 4:46-54)
3. The healing of the paralytic (see 5:1-9)
4. The multiplying of loaves and fish (see 6:1-14)
5. The healing of the man born blind (see 9:1-41)
6. The raising of Lazarus from the dead (see 11:17-44)
7. The resurrection of Jesus (see 20:1-18)

Step 2: Video Presentation (30-35 minutes)

"In the Beginning": Jesus at the Center (John 1:1-18)

I. Introduction to the Gospel of John

    A. Different from the other three Gospels

        1. Takes us into a different world, a "high mountain" perspective

        2. Differs in style, stories, structure, major themes

        3. Final Gospel written, by the "Beloved Disciple" (John)

II. Three Keys for Unlocking the Mystery of the Gospel of John

    A. Stage on which Jesus appears

        1. Similar to a play, where one first observes the setting

            a. Luke's Gospel begins with Zechariah going into the Temple to offer sacrifice

            b. Mark's Gospel opens in the desert with John the Baptist preparing the way of the Messiah, to the prophecy of Isaiah – "a voice crying out in the wilderness"

    c. Matthew's Gospel opens with the royal genealogy; shows Jesus' ancestry from David back to Abraham

  2. John's Gospel begins with: "In the beginning was the Word ..."

    a. St. Augustine: "These words are worthy of being written in gold and placed in every church around the world"

    b. Refer to the opening line of Genesis, the very first words of the Bible

    c. Reflection on the mystery of God's inner life: "and the Word was made flesh and dwelt among us" (1:14) – "dwelt" = God's holy presence among the people in the Tabernacle

B. Theme of signs

  1. Miracles as "signs" in John's Gospel that tell us something about Jesus – who he is

  2. "Book of Signs" – six miracles in the first eleven chapters

    a. Wedding feast at Cana (see 2:11) – "the first of his [Jesus'] signs"

    b. Healing of the royal official's son (see 4:54)

    c. Healing of the paralyzed man at the pool (see John 5)

    d. Feeding of the five thousand (see John 6)

  e. Restoring sight to the blind man (see John 9)

  f. Raising Lazarus from the dead (see John 11)

 3. Jesus enters Jerusalem to be glorified – his passion, death, and resurrection as seventh miracle

 4. Second half of John (John 12–21) = "Book of Glory"

 5. Different responses to Jesus' signs

C. "I am" statements

 1. Jesus says "I am" seven times in John's Gospel, each time making a profound statement about himself

  a. "I am the bread of life" (6:35)

  b. "I am the light of the world" (8:12)

  c. "I am the door [gate] of the sheep" (10:7)

  d. "I am the good shepherd" (10:11)

  e. "I am the resurrection and the life" (11:25)

    f. "I am the way, and the truth, and the life" (14:6)

    g. "I am the true vine" (15:1)

2. "I and the Father are one" (10:30)

    a. Jesus claims to be God

    b. No other major religious leader (Muhammad, Confucius, Buddha) claimed divinity

    c. Made in reaction to Jewish religious leaders who condemned Jesus for blasphemy, for claiming to be God

3. "Before Abraham was, I am" (8:58) – uses divine name (YHWH), revealed to Moses at the burning bush (see Exodus 3) and applies it to himself

4. Some see Jesus merely as a "wise sage" or a "good man" – if he is God, we must accept the entire package

– Takeaways –

1. Jesus reveals that he is more than a great prophet, wonder-worker, or teacher. He is the eternal Son of God, the "Word made flesh" (John 1:14).

2. Jesus challenges you to make a choice: Who is Jesus for you?

Step 3: Small-Group Fellowship (30-40 minutes)

Discussion Questions

1. Most people in the modern world believe in God. What are some of the common ways people think of God today?

_____

_____

_____

_____

_____

2. How are those views different from what the Bible reveals about God?

_____

_____

_____

_____

_____

3. Do you really believe God wants a personal relationship with you? Do you believe God loves you and wants to help you, forgive you, heal you, and care for all your needs? What are some of the things that make it difficult sometimes for you to believe in this personal God?

_____

_____

_____

_____

_____

4. Not everyone in John's Gospel sees in Jesus the divine Son of God. How do the following people view him?

    a. Nicodemus: "Rabbi, we know that you are a teacher" (John 3:2).

    _____

    _____

    b. The paralyzed man after he is healed by Jesus: "The man who healed me said to me, 'Take up your pallet, and walk'" (John 5:11).

    _____

    _____

    c. The crowds after the feeding of the multitude: "This is indeed the prophet who is to come into the world!" (John 6:14).

    _____

    _____

    d. The crowds in Jerusalem: "Is not this the man whom they seek to kill?" (John 7:25).

    _____

    _____

    e. Pilate: "Here is the man!" (John 19:5).

    _____

    _____

5. In what ways do people today think of Jesus as a mere man?

_____

_____

_____

_____

_____

_____

_____

6. What does John's Gospel reveal about Jesus' identity? How is this different from most modern conceptions about him? Consider the following passages:

   a. **John 1:1-3, 14:** "In the beginning was the Word, and the Word was with God, and the Word was God. He was in the beginning with God; all things were made through him, and without him was not anything made that was made. ... And the Word became flesh and dwelt among us." What does this tell us about Jesus? Is Jesus merely a man?

   _____

   _____

   _____

   _____

   b. **John 10:30, NAB:** "The Father and I are one." What is Jesus saying about himself? How do the Jewish leaders understand this statement? (See John 10:31-33.)

   _____

   _____

   _____

   _____

   c. **John 8:58:** "Before Abraham was, I am." Based on the video presentation, what is the significance of "I am"? How do the Jewish leaders respond to this statement?

   _____

   _____

   _____

   _____

7. Other religious leaders in the history of the world claimed to be prophets sent from God or messengers offering teachings about God or a way of life. How is Jesus portrayed as different in the following passages?

   a. Consider **John 14:6:** Jesus said, "I am the way, and the truth, and the life."

   _____

   _____

   _____

b. Consider **John 11:25-26:** Jesus said, "He who believes in me … shall never die."

_____

_____

_____

_____

8. Who is Jesus for you? What can you do to welcome Jesus as not just one part of your life, but as the very center of your life?

_____

_____

_____

_____

_____

_____

_____

The Last Supper, by Duccio

Closing Prayer

(5 minutes)

For our closing, let's pray together a portion of Pope Francis' prayer from *Evangelii Gaudium* ("The Joy of the Gospel"):

> *Lord, I have let myself be deceived; in a thousand ways I have shunned your love, yet here I am once more, to renew my covenant with you. I need you. Save me once again, Lord, take me once more into your redeeming embrace.*[1]

Step 4: Home Preparation – Looking Ahead

Read **John 1:19–2:25** and the **Session Two Overview** on page 14. As you read, consider the ways John the Baptist exemplifies the virtue of humility. Also notice what people say about Jesus in these scenes.

_____

_____

_____

_____

_____

_____

_____

_____

_____

_____

_____

_____

_____

_____

---

[1] Pope Francis, *Evangelii Gaudium* 3.

The Wedding Feast at Cana, by Paolo Veronese

Session Two

"Come and See": Becoming Disciples

John 1:19–2:25

 ❖

Session Overview

The Calling of Nathaniel,
Victoria Road United Reformed Church,
Newport, Wales

Do you ever feel you are just going through the motions with your faith?

Sometimes we can can "settle" into our lives as Christians. We go to church on Sundays. We follow the rules. We believe the right doctrines. We put some money in the collection basket. And we might even volunteer every once in a while at our parishes.

But Jesus wants us to do a lot more than follow the rules. He wants our hearts. He invites all of us to follow him as *disciples*.

A disciple does not just obey the master's teachings. The heart of discipleship is imitation of the master's way of life. So, when Jesus gathered his disciples, he was not inviting these men to be mere students, but to share his life and imitate his whole way of living. And Jesus invites us as disciples today, not just to follow his teachings, but to live like him, think like him, and serve like him.

"Come and see." That is what Jesus said to his first disciples in the Gospel of John. And he says the same thing to us today as he invites us to discipleship.

Step 1: Opening Review (5 minutes)

- In the last session, we saw that the view of God in John's Gospel is different from the way many people think about God today. Let's briefly review: What are some of those differences?

_____

_____

_____

_____

_____

We also discussed how the key to having a personal relationship with God is Jesus Christ. We saw that Jesus is not just one of the world's moral teachers or spiritual leaders. He is God, the God who became Man and died for us. Jesus invites us to have him as not just a part of our lives, but as the very center. And when we do that, we begin to experience the abundant life he promised us: "I came that [you] may have life, and have it abundantly!" (John 10:10).

In today's session, we will take a closer look at what it means to have a personal relationship with Jesus as we consider the topic of discipleship.

The Hour

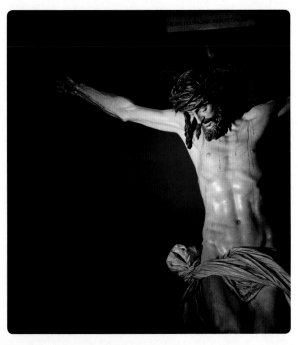

One of the central motifs in the Gospel of John is the repeated mention of "the hour." Like a drum beating in the background, readers of the first half of John's Gospel hear about a much-anticipated hour—an hour that is coming soon, that is, in a sense, already here (see John 4:23 and 5:25) but still has not yet come (see 2:4, 7:30, and 8:20). Only when he enters Jerusalem at the start of Holy Week, does Jesus finally announce that the hour has come and explain what the hour is. It is the hour of his glorious passion and death, when he will be raised up from the earth on the Cross, defeat the devil, and draw all men to himself (see 12:23-31).

Step 2: Video Presentation (30-35 minutes)

"Come and See": Becoming Disciples (John 1:19–2:25)

I. Being a Disciple of Jesus

    A. What is a disciple?

        1. In Jesus' time, a disciple was a student of a rabbi ("master," "teacher")

        2. Not like a modern teacher in a classroom

        3. The rabbi gathered disciples to share in his entire way of life and to live with him

    B. Jesus invites his disciples to share his life

        1. They were not just taking notes

        2. "There is more that is caught than taught"

        3. Jesus' way of life "rubbed off" on his disciples

        4. St. Paul – "be imitators of me, as I am of Christ" (1 Corinthians 11:1)

    C. Are you a disciple of Jesus?

        1. More than just attending Mass on Sunday

2. More than "following the rules"

3. Imitating the master

4. Basketball analogy – "following the rules" is just the beginning; one needs to develop the skills to be a good player

II. Jesus Gathers His First Two Disciples

A. Originally followers of John the Baptist

1. They follow Jesus after John calls him "the Lamb of God"

2. They are drawn to him

B. Jesus turns and asks: "What do you seek?" (1:38)

C. "Rabbi, where are you staying?"

1. A disciple shares life with the rabbi

2. They are asking to be Jesus' disciples by this question

III. Humility as Key Quality of Discipleship

A. Humility = understanding the truth about oneself

1. I need Jesus

    2. I see myself for what I am

    3. I see God's grace at work in my life

    4. I acknowledge my weaknesses

B. "[Without] me you can do nothing" (15:5) – complete dependence on God

C. Obstacles to humility

    1. Pride

    2. Vanity = worrying about what others think

    3. Envy = sorrow at the success of others

D. Exemplar of humility in John the Baptist (see John 1)

E. Humility = seeing your place and taking it; doing what God wants you to do

IV. Mary as Model Disciple

A. Wedding feast at Cana (see 2:1-11)

    1. "Woman, what is that to you and me? My hour has not yet come" (2:4)

    2. Not a rebuke to his mother

        a. Mary interprets it positively

    b. She tells the servants to "do whatever he tells you" (2:5)

3. Great significance to Jesus calling his mother "woman"

    a. Harkens back to the promise to Eve in Genesis (see 3:15)

    b. Referred to a "woman" whose descendant would crush the head of the Serpent, the devil

    c. Mary is the fulfillment of this prophecy

4. "My hour has not yet come" (2:4)

    a. Reference to his passion and death

    b. Final defeat of the devil on the Cross

5. Note the servants' trust and prompt obedience

6. Christ's glory is revealed in this first sign

– *Takeaways* –

1. Jesus wants you to follow him as his disciple.

2. May every person I come in contact with look up and see not me, but Jesus radiating through me.

Step 3: Small-Group Fellowship (30-40 minutes)

Discussion Questions

1. In this session, we saw how we, like Peter, Andrew, and John, are called to follow Jesus as disciples. How is being a disciple different from being a student?

_____

_____

_____

_____

2. Humility is a foundational quality of a disciple. Read **John 1:14.** How does Jesus himself model humility?

_____

_____

_____

_____

3. What are some of the ways John the Baptist exemplifies humility? Read **John 1:19-37.**

_____

_____

_____

_____

4. What are some ways we can imitate John the Baptist's humility more in our own lives?

_____

_____

_____

_____

Step 1: Opening Review (5 minutes)

- In the last session, we talked about what it means to be a disciple. What are the differences between being a disciple and being just a student?

<u>Student – learns & studies</u>

<u>disciple – embraces way of life, emulates Rabbi</u>

Now, as we begin walking through the next section of John's Gospel, we will see how Jesus draws his disciples close to himself by helping them discover their hearts' deepest longings, or thirsts, which are for him.

"Give Me a Drink"

Jesus asks for a drink two times in the Gospel of John: at the well with the Samaritan woman, when he says, "Give me a drink" (4:7), and at the Cross, when he says, "I thirst" (19:28). Blessed Teresa of Calcutta (Mother Teresa) saw in these words Jesus' thirst, not for water, but for our souls: for our attention, our devotion, and our love.

At this most difficult time, he proclaimed, "I thirst." And people thought he was thirsty in an ordinary way and they gave him vinegar straight away; but it was not for that thirst; it was for our love, our affection, that intimate attachment to him, and that sharing of his passion. He used, "I thirst," instead of, "Give me your love" … "I thirst." Let us hear him saying it to me and saying it to you.[1]

---

1   Joseph Langford, *Mother Teresa's Secret Fire* (Huntington, IN: Our Sunday Visitor, 2008), 281-282.

Step 2: Video Presentation (30-35 minutes)

At the Well: Our Deepest Thirst (John 3:1–4:42)

I. **Nicodemus (see 3:1-21)** *recog miracles not Jesus true being*

    A. "Man" of the Pharisees

        1. "Ruler of Jews"

        2. Member of the Sanhedrin

    B. Came to Jesus "at night"

        1. Light versus darkness – key contrast in John

        2. Jesus as light to dispel the darkness

        3. Judas leaves the Last Supper "at night"

    C. Born "anew" or "from above" (Gk., *anōthen*)

        1. This is necessary to enter into the kingdom of God (see 3:3)

        2. One must be born of "water" and the "spirit" (3:5)

        3. Spiritual rebirth through baptism

    D. Nicodemus' lack of humility in approaching Jesus

        1. Humility = fundamental quality of a disciple

2. He acts prideful, as a ruler of the Jews

3. He attempts to control the interaction

4. How do we approach Jesus in prayer?

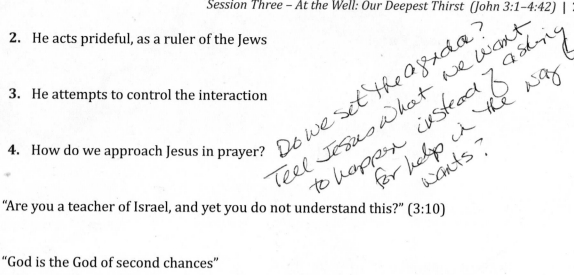

Do we set the agenda? Tell Jesus what we want to happen instead of asking God for help in the way God wants?

E. "Are you a teacher of Israel, and yet you do not understand this?" (3:10)

F. "God is the God of second chances"

1. Nicodemus' first encounter with Jesus does not go well

2. Ultimately, he is converted

3. He later defends Jesus to the Sanhedrin

4. He is at the Cross, and then he buries Jesus

II. The Woman at the Well (see 4:7–4:30)

A. Jesus passes through Samaria on the way to Galilee

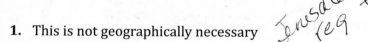

Jerusalem → Galilee not Samaria. (eg to go through)

1. This is not geographically necessary

2. It is intentional, "driven by mission"

B. He goes to Jacob's well and meets the Samaritan woman

1. At the "sixth hour" = noon

2. In the Old Testament, there were many "meetings" of man and woman at a well

  a. Jacob meets Rachel

  b. Moses meet Zipporah

  c. Isaac's servent meets Rebekah

  d. Marriage theme

C. Contrasts this meeting with Nicodemus

  1. Woman at the well – sixth hour: noon = light

  2. Nicodemus – at night = darkness

D. Response of the Samaritan woman

  1. Surprise at Jesus speaking to her

   a. Samaritan

   b. A woman

  2. "Jews have no dealings with Samaritans" (4:9)

E. Living (flowing) water *(Hydōr zōn)*

F. Water of eternal life

G. Jesus meets her where she is

  1. Her deeper thirst is for love

2. Only God can give this

H. Jesus asks the woman to bring her husband

    1. "Five husbands" of the woman

    2. Symbolizes the Samaritans intermarrying with five pagan nations

        a. Turning to cultic deities

        b. Called to worship YHWH

        c. Prophecy of God's coming as Bridegroom

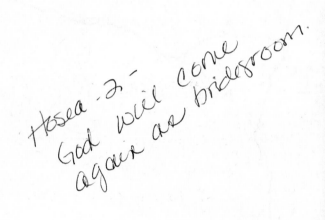

Hosea - 3 -
God will come
again as bridegroom.

    3. Woman perceives Jesus is a prophet

    4. Jesus reveals to her that he is the Messiah

I. The woman becomes the "first evangelist"

    1. People of the town come to believe in Jesus

– *Takeaways* –

1. God alone can satisfy the deepest desires of our hearts.

2. No matter how far we have wandered from him, Jesus goes out of his way to meet us with his mercy.

Step 3: Small-Group Fellowship (30-40 minutes)

Discussion Questions

1. Read **John 3:2.** According to this verse, what is Nicodemus' understanding of Jesus?

   Nicodemus believes Jesus is a teacher from God

2. Consider how others in the Gospel of John understand Jesus in the following verses:

   a. John 1:29 (John the Baptist):

   Lamb of God

   b. John 1:41 (Andrew):

   Messiah

   c. John 1:45 (Philip):

   Prophet

   d. John 1:49 (Nathaniel):

   Son of God

3. Jesus says, "Unless one is born anew, he cannot see the kingdom of God" (John 3:3). The Greek word for "anew" *(anōthen)* can mean "again" or "from above."

   a. Read **John 3:4.** How does Nicodemus understand Jesus' words?

   a physical rebirth

b. Read **John 3:5-7.** What does Jesus mean by being born *anōthen?*

Born of the Spirit

4. Compare and contrast Nicodemus and the Samaritan woman.

    a. What are the differences in the way John's Gospel introduces Nicodemus in John 3:1-2 and the Samaritan woman in John 4:6-7? (Note that "the sixth hour" is noon.)

Nicodemus	Samaritan Woman
Night	Noon
Knew Jesus was from God	Didn't know who he was
Sought Jesus	Encountered Jesus

    b. How well would a man like Nicodemus be respected in his community? (See John 3:1, 10.) How well would a woman like the one Jesus meets at the well be respected in her community? Read **John 4:16-18.**

Nicodemus- highly respected

Woman- Shunned - @ well @ noon

    c. How well does Nicodemus understand Jesus? How well does the Samaritan woman understand Jesus?

Samaritan woman u'stands him @ the end

5. Jesus speaks to the woman, giving her "living water." The Greek expression translated "living water" is *hydōr zōn,* a term that can be understood on the natural level as "flowing water"—water that is good and fresh to drink—or it can have a more supernatural significance as water that gives spiritual life and blessing (see Isaiah 44:3; Jeremiah 2:13, 17:13; and Zechariah 14:8).

    a. Read **John 7:37-38.** What does Jesus mean by "living water"?

He is the living water.

b. Read **John 4:13-15.** How does the woman understand Jesus' words about "living water"?

She thinks it's water that is boiled.

6. Every human person is created with a deep hunger and thirst for God. Psalm 42:1-2 expresses the deep thirst every human person has: "As a hart longs for flowing streams, so longs my soul for thee, O God. My soul thirsts for God, for the living God."

    a. Where has the woman been trying to satiate her thirst?

    By looking for love w/ many men

    b. Read **John 4:16.** How does Jesus use the woman's desire for running water to point to her deeper thirst?

    He likened her thirst to the desire for God.

7. What are the things people thirst for today that distract them from the deepest thirst of the human heart?

    Recognition, money, friends,

Fr. Edward Meeks.

Session Three – At the Well: Our Deepest Thirst (John 3:1–4:42)_ | **33**

8. St. Augustine once prayed about the profound thirst every person has for God, saying, "You have made us for yourself, and our heart is restless until it rests in you" (CCC 30).[2]

   a. How might this prayer shed light on the restlessness many people have today?

   So many of us are removed from God and this void is causing dissatisfaction.

   b. Are you anxious, worried, or restless about anything right now? How might this prayer of St. Augustine apply to you?

   BK, NK, twins,

9. Jesus "had to pass" through Samaria. According to the video presentation, what does this tell us about God's thirst for us?

   He made a choice to go through Samaria for conversion of hearts.

10. _What do you thirst for most in life?_

---

[2] St. Augustine, _Conf._ 1, 1, 1: PL 32, 659-661.

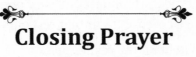

Closing Prayer

(5 minutes)

For our closing, let us think about our thirst for God and pray Psalm 42:1-2, 6-8, and 11.

As a hart longs for flowing streams, so longs my soul for thee, O God.

My soul thirsts for God, for the living God. When shall I come and behold the face of God? ...

My soul is cast down within me, therefore I remember thee

from the land of Jordan and of Hermon, from Mount Mizar.

Deep calls to deep at the thunder of thy cataracts;

all thy waves and thy billows have gone over me.

By day the Lord commands his steadfast love;

and at night his song is within me, a prayer to the God of my life.

Why are you cast down, O my soul, and why are you disquieted within me?

Hope in God; for I shall again praise him, my help and my God.

Step 4: Home Preparation – Looking Ahead

Read **John 4:43–6:71** and the **Session Four Overview** on page 36. When reading these passages, consider the different ways the following characters trust in Jesus' words: the royal official, the paralyzed man, the crowds during the Bread of Life discourse, and Peter.

_____

_____

_____

_____

_____

_____

_____

_____

_____

_____

_____

_____

_____

Christ in the Storm on the Sea of Galilee, by Ludolf Backhuysen

"Believe in Me": **Trust and Surrender**

John 4:43–6:71

Session Overview

Healing the Paralytic, by Anthony van Dyck

It is easy to say we believe in Jesus. It is harder to really mean it. And it is very challenging to entrust our lives to him.

Belief has two aspects. To believe in God means we are intellectually convinced God exists and our minds assent to all God has revealed. Believing also means entrusting ourselves to God (see CCC 150). So, when we say, "I believe in Jesus," we are not just affirming that Jesus exists, that he is the Son of God, and that he died for our sins. We are not just affirming that he is our Lord and Savior. When we say we believe in Jesus, we are entrusting our entire lives to him.

In this next section of John's Gospel, Jesus tests various people's faith in him. He tests the royal official whose son is dying, the man who has been paralyzed for thirty-eight years, and the crowds who struggle to believe in the Eucharist. He also tests the faith of his own disciples, especially Philip, Andrew, and Peter. And we will see how these lessons in faith and trust are just as applicable for our lives today. Just as Jesus challenged his followers to entrust themselves completely to him, so he is inviting us to surrender our lives to his direction, care, and protection. The more we trust in him, the more we will experience his love guiding and sustaining us in all we do.

Step 1: Opening Review (5 minutes)

- In the last session, we considered the Samaritan woman's encounter with Jesus. Where is the Samaritan woman trying to satiate her thirst?

  at the well (literally)
  through her many husbands (figuratively)

- What does Jesus offer her to satiate her thirst? Read John 4:10-13.

  Living Water – Christ

- What might this story tell us about our thirst for love and happiness?

  We often try to satisfy ourselves
  by looking to the wrong things – material, etc.

In this next section of John's Gospel, we will consider another major theme of the Christian life: trusting God with our entire lives.

Abiding in Jesus

He who eats my flesh and drinks my blood abides in me, and I in him" (John 6:56). The idea of abiding expresses the profound unity Jesus wants to share with his disciples. While the term "abide" initially described the disciples as simply staying in the same dwelling with Jesus (see 1:38-39), Jesus uses the word to characterize his disciples as those who abide in his teachings (see 8:31) and who abide in his love by obeying his commandments (see 15:4-10). Christ's followers have allowed Jesus' teachings and his love to take up residence in their hearts. This is possible because Jesus even promises his disciples that the Spirit will take up residence (abide) in them (see 14:17). In the Bread of Life discourse, Jesus refers to his dwelling within his disciples through the Eucharist. Those who do not partake of his Body and Blood, will have no life in them (see 6:53). But of those who eat his flesh and drink his Blood in the Eucharist, Jesus says he "abides in me, and I in him" (6:56).

Step 2: Video Presentation (30-35 minutes)

"Believe in Me": Trust and Surrender (John 4:43–6:71)

I. **Healing of the Royal Official's Son (4:43-54)**

    A. "Royal official" (4:46) – based on the Greek word used; he probably worked for Herod

        1. Walked fifteen miles from Capernaum to see Jesus

        2. Long journey to ask Jesus to heal his dying son

    B. Faith of those present *[handwritten: not just the official but the crowd.]*

        1. "Unless you [pl.] see signs and wonders you will not believe" (4:48)

        2. Official pleads with Jesus

        3. "Go, your son will live" (4:50)

            a. Note that Jesus does not go back to Capernaum with him

            b. He calls the man to trust his word ("The man believed the word that Jesus spoke to him")

    C. Message: turn to Jesus in our needs – he answers our prayers, not in the way we expect, not on our timetable

II. **Healing of the Paralyzed Man on the Sabbath (5:2-46)**

    A. "One man," ill for thirty-eight years

        1. Symbolizes Old Testament Israel

2. Israel's lack of trust in God during the Exodus

3. Result: Israel wandered in the desert for forty years

— wandered for 38 yrs after central recalcitrance.
readiness : recalcitrance.
Total of 40.

B. Five porticoes symbolize five books of the *Torah* (Law)

C. Jesus asks: "Do you want to be healed?" (5:6)

1. Deeper, spiritual meaning

2. We sometimes are attached to certain patterns of behavior

3. Do we really want to healed?

D. The man's lack of trust

— not spiritual — excuses).

1. Attempts to find a "human solution" in the waters of the pool

2. Contrasts faith of the royal official

3. The man is not thankful, lack of gratitude

4. He does not understand who Jesus is ("the man who healed me told me to take up my mat and walk")

E. Religious leaders plot to kill Jesus for healing on the Sabbath (see 5:16-18)

1. Turning point in John's Gospel

2. Jesus' response: "My father is working still, and I am working" (5:17) – makes himself equal with God

Creation today
Rested – 7 – but
did not create new,
but cont. to hold everything
he created together – still
wkg.

III. Multiplication of Loaves (6:1-14)

    A. Crowd follows Jesus because of the signs he performed

    B. Jesus singles out the disciples Philip and Andrew

        1. Among the first disciples of Jesus

        2. Witnessed the miracle at the wedding at Cana

        3. Should have trusted that Jesus could provide in a time of lack

        4. Look at the situation from a purely human perspective

    C. Jesus blesses five barley loaves and two fish – feeds five thousand

        1. Took the bread and gave thanks and distributed it (see 6:11)

        2. Foreshadows the Last Supper

        3. Passover is mentioned three times in John's Gospel

            a. Wedding at Cana

            b. Multiplication of loaves

            c. Last Supper

    D. Prefigures the Eucharist (*eucharisteō* = give thanks)

IV. Bread of Life Discourse (6:35-71)

    A. "Real presence" of Christ in the Eucharist – Body, Blood, Soul, Divinity

B. Greatest call to trust: to believe in the Eucharist

C. A "hard saying"

D. Peter's response (6:68) = "Lord, to whom shall we go? You have the words of eternal life ..."

    1. Though he does not understand, Peter trusts Jesus

E. Many disciples leave Jesus at this point

Begins using hyphenate eat literally or figuratively then to Trogo–Chew.

    1. Lack of understanding

    2. Lack of trust

F. "Walk by faith, not by sight" (2 Corinthians 5:7)

    1. In the Eucharist

    2. In our daily lives

    3. We need to trust in Jesus

– *Takeaways* –

1. We are called to believe in Christ and to entrust ourselves to him.

2. Will you believe in Christ's words, even when you do not fully understand them?

Step 3: Small-Group Fellowship (30-40 minutes)

Discussion Questions

1. The royal official walks fifteen miles to find Jesus in Cana and beg him to come to Capernaum to heal his dying son.

   a. Does Jesus answer the official's request?

   Jesus healed his son, but did not go w/ him to Capernaum

   b. What does this passage tell us about trusting God in prayer? Does Jesus always answer our prayers?

   The official trusted Jesus and went home. God answers prayers but not in our way / time.

2. All the other healings in John's Gospel involve Jesus being physically present to the person he heals. He commands the paralyzed man to walk (see John 5:8). He anoints the blind man's eyes with clay and restores his sight (see John 9:6-7). He goes to Lazarus' tomb to raise him from the dead (see John 11:38-44). But Jesus simply tells the royal official, "Go; your son will live" (John 4:50).

   a. What kind of faith is Jesus asking of the royal official?

   Faith w/o seeing — Faith in his word.

   b. How might this challenge your faith in Jesus? Is there an area of life that you have not surrendered to God's Word?

3. Jesus asks the paralyzed man at the pool, "Do you want to be healed?" It seems like the answer would be an obvious, "Yes."

   a. But read **John 5:7**. Does the man give a clear, "Yes, I want to be healed"?

   No, he explains why he cannot get to the water to be healed.

   b. Imagine Jesus standing before us and asking the same question about our weaknesses, sins, bad habits, and addictions: "Do you want to be healed?" Do you think everyone would give a wholehearted, "Yes, Jesus, please heal me!"? Or do you think some people would hesitate to give a total, "Yes"? Why?

   We might want to know what we would have to give up. Also give excuses about why we sin and are weak.

4. John 5:16-18 is a key turning point in the narrative of the fourth Gospel. The Jewish leaders seek to kill Jesus. What are the two main reasons the Jewish leaders want to kill him? Read **John 5:18**.

   1) Broke Sabbath
   2) Said God was his father

5. When five thousand people come to Jesus, he tests his apostles by saying, "How are we to buy bread, so that these people may eat?" (John 6:5). Let's consider how well the apostles do on this test.

   a. What is Philip's response? Read **John 6:7**.

   We don't have enough money to buy food for all these people.

   b. Read **John 6:8-9.** What is Andrew's response?

   There is a boy w/ loaves and fishes — but not nearly enough

c. Philip and Andrew were both at the wedding at Cana. What lesson should they have learned from Jesus' response to the lack of wine at the wedding?

That Jesus can perform miracles and they should trust in him.

6. Are there some areas in your life right now where you think you do not have enough—enough time, energy, resources, or love? What are those areas, and how might this scene in John's Gospel encourage you?

Jesus will ensure you have enough

7. In the Bread of Life discourse, Jesus gives some of his most profound teaching on his real presence in the Eucharist—the Eucharist is not just a symbol of Jesus, but is his actual Body and Blood. The Catholic Church teaches what the earliest Christians affirmed: that the bread and wine at Mass are changed into the Body and Blood of Christ. This is not a chemical change. All the outward, sensible appearances of bread and wine remain. But underneath those outward appearances, Jesus' very Body and Blood is present. Let us consider what this passage might tell us about the Eucharist.

a. Jesus says he is "the bread of life" (John 6:35) and that, "if anyone eats of this bread, he will live forever; and the bread which I shall give for the life of the world is my flesh" (6:51). Read **John 6:52.** How do the Jews interpret Jesus' words? Do they think he is speaking figuratively (as a metaphor about nourishing their souls on Jesus' words) or realistically (about actually partaking of Jesus' flesh)?

b. How does Jesus respond to their objection? Read **John 6:53-56.** Does Jesus attempt to back up and clarify, saying, "No, you misunderstood. I was only speaking metaphorically here"?

No, he repeats what he has said w/o explaining further.

8. This teaching requires great faith. It is too hard for many of Jesus' own disciples, who decide to leave him over this teaching (see John 6:66). Jesus asks the Twelve if they also will leave. Read **John 6:60 and 6:67-68.**

   a. Who reflects a greater intellectual understanding of Jesus' teaching on the Eucharist—the many disciples in 6:60 or Peter in 6:68?

   words of everlasting life

   _____

   _____

   b. What is the difference between the way the many disciples and Simon Peter respond to Jesus after his teaching on the Eucharist?

   leave because they don't understand / has faith in Jesus)

   _____

   _____

9. How might Peter's example inspire us to trust more in Jesus' word? Do you trust Jesus' word in the Scriptures and the way he guides us today through the teachings of the Catholic Church? Is there a certain teaching of the Church that you struggle to put into practice? If so, what can you do this week to put more of your trust in God's Word, even if you struggle to grasp it completely?

   _____

   _____

   _____

Closing Prayer

(5 minutes)

Lord Jesus, we love you. We want to put our trust in you. But we admit we are afraid ... afraid to let go of certain things, afraid to let go of control. Help us to be more like the royal official and St. Peter, who put their trust in your words even when they did not fully understand them. We take a moment now, here in your presence, in the silence of our hearts, to tell you about one area of our lives that we want to entrust more to you.

We entrust our lives to you and our heavenly Father as we say, "Our Father ..."

Step 4: Home Preparation – Looking Ahead

Read **John 7–9** and the **Session Five Overview** on page 48. While reading these passages, notice the mounting opposition to Jesus in Jerusalem. At the same time, consider how Jesus' mercy and love is manifested so beautifully, especially with the woman caught in adultery and the man born blind.

_____

_____

_____

_____

_____

_____

_____

_____

_____

_____

_____

_____

_____

Christ and the Pauper: Healing of the Blind Man, by A. N. Mironov

Session Five

Encountering Mercy

John 7–9

Session Overview

Image of the Divine Mercy, by Eugene Kazimirowski

Being a follower of Jesus means constantly relying on his mercy. And we will see in this session that his Divine Mercy has two main parts: forgiveness and healing.

On one hand, Jesus *forgives* us of our sins. He comes not to point fingers or condemn. He longs to be reunited with all who have turned away from him. He reaches out to us with his mercy as he did to the woman caught in adultery. "Neither do I condemn you; go and do not sin again" (John 8:11).

But on the other hand, mercy is not just about sins being forgiven. It is also about *healing the roots of sin.* Jesus wants to heal us of our weaknesses, remedy our bad habits, and mend our deepest wounds. Just as he made the deaf hear, so he enables us to hear his voice more profoundly in certain areas of our lives. Just as Jesus made the paralyzed man walk, so he helps those who feel paralyzed by their weaknesses and unable to change to be able rise above their sins and walk in his ways. And just as he cured a man who had been born blind, Jesus continues to bestow his mercy on us today by healing us of our spiritual blindness so we can begin to see more like he sees.

In this session, we will see how just as the opposition to Jesus in Jerusalem intensifies, Jesus' mercy manifests itself even more brilliantly: first on the woman caught in adultery and then on the man born blind. Let's consider how we can see ourselves in these two characters and how we can encounter God's mercy more profoundly in our lives today.

Step 1: Opening Review (5 minutes)

- In the last session, we discussed the theme of trust. Let's briefly review: How did the following characters model trust for us: the royal official whose son was dying (see John 4:46-53) and Peter at the end of the Bread of Life discourse (see John 6:60-66)?

  Trusted Jesus even though his son was not present and he confident and see his healing.

  Did not ustd but trusted Jesus as the Saviour.

- How do Philip and Andrew demonstrate a lack of trust when Jesus wants to feed the five thousand (see John 6:7-9)?

  Yes. They don't see his ability to work the miracle of feeding the multitudes. The answer doesn't enter their minds

Now, in today's session, we will consider Jesus' mercy and see how he not only offers us forgiveness but also healing.

The Feasts in John's Gospel

Three Jewish feasts feature prominently in the Gospel of John:

1. The Feast of Passover (see 2:13, 6:4, and 11:55ff)

2. The Feast of Tabernacles (see 7:2)

3. The Feast of Dedication of the Temple, commonly called Hanukkah (see 10:22)

In the fourth Gospel, these Jewish feasts serve not just as chronological markers; the narrative draws on the rituals and the meanings of the feasts to teach people about Jesus. For example, while the Feast of Dedication celebrated the Temple, John's Gospel underscores how Jesus' body is now the true temple (see John 2:21). Just as the Feast of Tabernacles involved a memorable light ceremony and water ritual, Jesus declares during this feast that he is the true light of the world and the source of living water (see 7:37-38, 8:12, and 9:5). Just as the lamb was sacrificed for Passover to recall that first Passover when Israel was liberated from slavery in Egypt, so Jesus is "the Lamb of God" who dies as the new Passover Lamb on the Cross to liberate us from slavery to sin and death.

Step 2: Video Presentation (30-35 minutes)

Encountering Mercy (John 7–9)

I.   **Feast of Tabernacles (7:1-53)**

   A. Seven-day feast

      1. Pilgrimage feast to Jerusalem

      2. People dwelled in tents around the city

   B. Celebrates three main elements

      1. Looked to the past

         a. Remembrance/reenactment of the Exodus event

         b. Israel dwelled in tents during its forty-year journey to the Promised Land

      2. Present — *Dedication of Tabernacle → Feast of the Tabernacles.*

         a. During the Exodus, God's presence was in the Tabernacle

         b. In the Promised Land, the divine presence was in the Temple built by Solomon

         c. God's presence left the Temple when it was destroyed by Babylon in 586 BC (see Ezekiel 10–11)

         d. God's presence did not return to the Temple when it was rebuilt

3. Looked to the future

    a. Hope that God's presence would return again (see Ezekiel 47)

    b. Vision of life-giving river flowing from the Temple, bringing healing

C. Two main ceremonies/rituals

    1. Water ceremony

        a. For seven days, the priests draw water from the pool of Siloam

        b. Process to the Temple and pour water in a tube on the altar

        c. Prophecy of Zechariah 14:8 – God will come; all nations will worship God; living waters will flow from Jerusalem

    2. Light ceremony

        a. Priest lights four large menorahs, illuminating the Temple

    3. "If any one thirst, let him come to me and drink ... 'Out of [my] heart shall flow rivers of living water'" (7:37-38)

        a. Jesus' heart is the new Temple

        b. Will bring new life and healing

    4. "I am light of the world" (8:12)

        a. One of seven "I am" statements

    b. Significant during the Feast of Tabernacles: Jesus says these words in the Temple treasury, next to where the light ceremony takes place

II. Woman Caught in Adultery (8:2-12)

    A. Pharisees attempt to trap Jesus

        1. To pit the Jewish law (stoning a woman caught in adultery) against the Roman law (forbidding Jews to apply the death penalty without permission)

        2. Jesus avoids the trap: "Let him who is without sin" cast the first stone (8:7)

        3. The Pharisees, who see themselves as without sin, are shown to be sinful by their response

        4. Jesus is the only one present "without sin"

            a. He could justly cast the first stone

            b. Instead, he responds with mercy

            c. "Woman ... has no one condemned you? ... Neither do I condemn you; go, and do not sin again" (8:10)

    B. Profound mercy of Jesus, followed by call to conversion: "Go, and do not sin again"

    C. Why does Jesus write on the ground?

        1. Jeremiah 17:13: The names of those who turn away will be written in the dust, because they have forsaken the LORD, who is the spring of living water

Apostles – knock dust from their feet.

        2. Zechariah 13:1 – Fountain of flowing water from Jerusalem for forgiveness of sins

III. Healing of the Blind Man (9:1-12)

    A. Day-night, light-darkness imagery

        1. Reference to the Feast of Tabernacles

    B. Jesus uses clay and tells the blind man to wash in the pool of Siloam (see 9:6-7)

        1. In Genesis, Adam was formed from clay

        2. Siloam (literally "sent")

            a. Same pool from which priests draw water for Feast of Tabernacles

        3. Baptismal imagery

IV. Both Stories Highlight Two Aspects of God's Mercy

    A. Forgiveness

    B. Conversion

– Takeaways –

1. Jesus, in his mercy, offers us forgiveness and healing.

2. Allow Christ's mercy to change you so you can be more like him.

Step 3: Small-Group Fellowship (30-40 minutes)
Discussion Questions

1. All the stories from this session take place around the Feast of Tabernacles celebration in Jerusalem.

    a. What two key events from Israel's history does this feast recall?

    Exodus from Egypt, Harvest
    40 years in the desert
    Dedication of Temple in Jerusalem

    b. What future hope did this feast express for Israel? Read **Zechariah 14:16-17**.

    Return of God to Jerusalem - and recognition and
    worship of all nations - healing
    Hope for the future

    c. What does this tell us about Jesus going to Jerusalem for the Feast of Tabernacles?

    Jesus is the new Temple / living water /
    light of the world

2. The video presentation mentioned two dramatic ceremonies associated with the Feast of Tabernacles: the water ceremony and the light ceremony.

    a. What did the priests do in the water ceremony?

    Draw water from the pool of Siloam
    and pour it on the altar of the
    temple

Lev 23 ⟩ Explains the
Deut 16 ⟩ main feasts.

b. What did the light ceremony entail?

lighting large menorah and
illuminating temple

c. Read **Zechariah 14:6-8.** How might the water ceremony and the light ceremony express these prophetic hopes of Zechariah?

1) lighting the darkness
2) living waters go out from Jerusalem
3) Lord shall be king over all the Earth

3. How does this Feast of Tabernacles background shed light on Jesus' words in **John 7:37** and **John 8:12?**

If any man thirst let him come to me and drink

I am the light of the world. He that followeth me walketh not in darkness but shall have the light of life

4. How does the scene involving the woman caught in adultery demonstrate what the video presentation called "the two sides of Jesus' love"?

• Healing & forgiveness — God rescued her from her sin & guilt
  to chg our behavior.

Blind Man — Heals the man's infirmity — physical, spiritual

5. How might we experience both sides of Jesus' love in the sacrament of reconciliation?

- Forgiveness of Sins

- I firmly resolve w/ the help of your grace to confess my sins, to do penance and amend my life.

6. The video presentation discussed ways the story of the man born blind sheds light on the sacrament of baptism. What are some of those ways?

~~water~~ Spit mixed w/ clay was washed off in the pool of Siloam so he could see.

- Adam made from clay + spit.
- Wash in Siloam — means sent one

7. Read **John 9:2.** Imagine being the man born blind, sitting on the roadside begging for alms. Then, imagine hearing Jesus and the disciples passing by. You hear the disciples ask Jesus, "Who sinned, this man or his parents, that he was born blind?"

a. How would that question make you feel?

Shameful —

b. Read **John 9:3.** How would you feel hearing Jesus reply, "It was not that this man sinned, or his parents"?

Hopeful

c. Now, imagine Jesus anointing your eyes with the clay and you washing in the pool of Siloam and being able to see for the first time in your life. What would you ask Jesus to help you to see better in your life today?

Goodness in others.
My role in God's plan

The Woman Taken in Adultery, by Guercino

Closing Prayer

(5 minutes)

Prayerfully take a moment to think about a particular sin in your life. It could be something you said or did a long time ago or something you are doing right now.

Prayerfully imagine crowds of people accusing you of that sin, shouting at you and angrily condemning you. Suddenly, Jesus stands before you in the middle of the crowd. He silences them and looks you in the eye with tender love. Imagine him saying to you, "I do not condemn you." How would you respond to such mercy?

Next, imagine him saying to you, "Go, and do not sin again." What would you say to Jesus in return?

Step 4: Home Preparation – Looking Ahead

Read **John 10–12** and the **Session Six Overview** on page 60. Think about the qualities of the "good shepherd" described in John 10 and how Jesus exemplified those qualities throughout his life.

_____

_____

_____

_____

_____

_____

_____

_____

_____

_____

_____

_____

Christ in the House of Martha, attributed to Georg Friedrich Stettner

The Law of Self-Giving

John 10–12

Session Overview

The Raising of Lazarus, by Leon Bonnat

One of the great mysteries in life is that we find our fulfillment only when we give ourselves away in love. As St. John Paul II often taught, man finds himself only when he makes himself a sincere gift to others.[1] But this profound truth of our humanity is scary to modern man. We like to grasp at things for ourselves: more attention, more control, more security, more wealth, more "likes"—*How can I get the most out of life for myself?*

Jesus flips this modern mentality on its head and says, "He who loves his life loses it, and he who hates his life in this world will keep it for eternal life" (John 12:25). The more I grasp at life for my own gain, comfort, and pleasure, the more frustrated and disappointed I will be. But the more I give of myself in love to God, my wife, my kids, and my neighbor, the more my life will be enriched. I do not lose anything when I make my life a gift to others. I actually gain so much more, for God has made us for self-giving love, and it is the only way we will find true happiness in life.

This law of self-giving is written in the fabric of our humanity, and Jesus not only describes it; he models it for us. He says he is the "good shepherd" who lays down his life for his sheep (see John 10:14-15). Indeed, Jesus will raise his friend Lazarus from the dead, even though this miracle will infuriate the chief priests and impel them to put Jesus to death (see John 11:50). He will be like a grain of wheat that falls into the earth and dies in order to bear much fruit (see John 12:24), and he invites us to share in his life of total self-giving.

---

[1] *Gaudium et Spes* (GS) 24.

Step 1: Opening Review (5 minutes)

- The previous session focused on the theme of mercy in the Christian life. We saw that there are two aspects of mercy. What are those two aspects? And how are they exemplified in the woman caught in adultery and the man born blind?

_____

_____

_____

_____

_____

_____

_____

_____

In today's session, we will consider a profound mystery about life that Jesus teaches and models for us in John 10–12. "He who loves his life loses it, and he who hates his life in this world will keep it for eternal life" (John 12:25). We will now explore what Jesus means by this and the reason following this teaching is the pathway to true happiness.

The Seven "I Am" Statements

John's Gospel also features seven profound statements Jesus makes about himself, each beginning with the words "I am."

1. "I am the bread of life" (6:35, 48, 51).

2. "I am the light of the world" (8:12, 9:5).

3. "I am the door of the sheep" (10:7, 9).

4. "I am the good shepherd" (10:11, 14).

5. "I am the resurrection and the life" (11:25).

6. "I am the way, and the truth, and the life" (14:6).

7. "I am the true vine" (15:1).

Step 2: Video Presentation (30-35 minutes)

The Law of Self-Giving (John 10–12)

VIII.   **Good Shepherd (10:11-18)**

    A.   Shepherds play a prominent role in the Bible

        1.   David – fought lions to protect his sheep

        2.   Micah 5 – prophecy regarding the future King (Shepherd) of Israel

        3.   Ezekiel 34

            a.   The wicked shepherds (religious leaders) who did not feed the sheep

            b.   "I myself will be the shepherd of my sheep …" (Ezekiel 34:15) *— wicked shepherd / weak not str etc. vs good shepherd*

            c.   Prophecy of the Messiah

    B.   "I am the good shepherd" (John 10:11) – three characteristics

        1.   Lays down his life for the sheep (see John 10:11)

        2.   Voluntarily gives up his life – "no one takes it from me" (10:18)

        3.   His sheep will know his voice and follow him (see 10:27)

IX.   Raising of Lazarus (11:1-53)

    A.   Every other sign in John leads up to this one

        1.   Turning point in John's Gospel

        2.   Catalyst for Christ's crucifixion

    3. Foreshadows the resurrection of Jesus

    4. Crowds are amazed, and the story spreads

    5. Gets the attention of Caiaphas and the priests, who begin to plot against Jesus

B. Relationship between Jesus and Lazarus

    1. "[Lord], the one you love is ill" (John 11:3, NAB)

    2. Jesus loves him, yet delays two days (see 11:1-6)

        a. Why? "This illness is not unto death; it is for the glory of God" (11:4)

    3. Refers to Lazarus as "our friend" (11:11)

        a. Words of Jesus at Last Supper: no greater love than to lay down one's life for one's friend (see 15:13)

        b. Christ will lay down his life – for his friend Lazarus and us

C. Lazarus' sisters

    1. Martha meets Jesus outside, Mary remains in the house (see 11:20)

    2. Mary as a model disciple, responds immediately to his call, goes out (see 11:28) and she sits at Jesus' feet (see 11:32)

        "knows his voice" [handwritten annotation]

D. "Lazarus, come out" (11:43)

    1. Jesus, the Good Shepherd, calls his sheep by name

    2. His sheep know his voice and follow him; he leads them out

    3. John 10 and 11 – not separate stories but linked in the image of the Good Shepherd

E. St. Augustine: raising of Lazarus is a symbol of confession

    1. Lazarus comes out "bound" in bandages

    2. Jesus commands "unbind him"

    3. In confession, we come "bound" and leave "unbound"

    4. Words of absolution: "I absolve you from your sins ..."

F. Jesus' resurrection foreshadowed

    1. Stone rolled away from the tomb

    2. Women go to the tomb weeping

    3. Apostles see Jesus' burial clothes; crowd sees wrappings of Lazarus

G. Jesus calls us to be unbound

    1. From our own sinfulness

    2. In the sacrament of reconciliation

H. Priests plot Jesus' death

    1. They fear intervention of the Romans (see 11:48)

    2. Annual messianic fervor around Passover led to heightened Roman vigilance, extra forces in Jerusalem

    3. High priest: Better for one man (Jesus) to die than the entire nation (see 11:51)

III. Book of Glory Begins

A. Jesus enters Jerusalem, riding on a donkey, to the acclaim of the crowds

B. "The hour has come for the Son of man to be glorified" (12:23-25)

C. Jesus clarifies what "glory" means:

   1. A "grain of wheat" must die to bear much fruit – offers his life for the salvation of the world

   2. Jesus gives his life up willingly for the sake of all

   3. "Whoever loses his life for my sake ..." (Mark 8:35)

D. The law of self-giving

   1. St. John Paul II: "Man finds himself through a sincere gift of self" to others[2]

   2. "Logic of love" = when I give, I gain

E. "The ruler of this world [will] be cast down" (12:31)

   1. Defeat of Satan by the death of Christ on the Cross

   2. Liberation of man from sin and death

   3. Shows us how to live the law of self-giving

– Takeaways –

1. Jesus is the Good Shepherd who lays down his life for his sheep—for you.

2. When we give of ourselves to others, we find true happiness.

---

[2] GS 24.

Step 3: Small-Group Fellowship (30-40 minutes)

Discussion Questions

1. Jesus is the Good Shepherd. What are the qualities of a good shepherd? How is this different from the wicked shepherds prophesied by Ezekiel? Read **Ezekiel 34:1-6.** Who are the wicked shepherds in Jesus' day?

   Protects his flock,
   Risk himself for the flock

2. In the Good Shepherd discourse, Jesus also talks about two qualities of his sheep. "My sheep hear my voice … and they follow me" (John 10:27). What are some ways we can come to know Christ's voice better? What are some ways we can "follow" our Good Shepherd better?

   Recognize Gods voice
   Hear ; heed his call

3. Based on the video presentation, how does the story of Lazarus being raised from the dead shed light on the sacrament of reconciliation (commonly known as "confession")?

Freedom from death

"   "   Sin

living again.

"called by Jesus"

Entry of Christ into Jerusalem, by Anthony van Dyck

4. How is the raising of Lazarus a key impetus for Christ's death on the Cross? Why do the Jewish leaders want to kill Jesus after this incident? Read **John 11:45-53.**

_____

_____

_____

_____

_____

_____

_____

_____

_____

_____

5. Throughout John's Gospel, Jesus speaks about his approaching "hour." That hour finally arrives in John 12. What is this "hour" of Jesus? What does Jesus say will happen in this hour? Read **John 12:23-24, 31-33.**

_____

_____

_____

_____

_____

_____

_____

_____

_____

6. With ordinary transactions in life, when we give something away, we do not have it anymore. If I give you ten dollars, I do not have that ten-dollar bill anymore. But with love, it is different. When I give myself in love to God and to others, I do not lose anything. I actually increase in love and thus grow in happiness. St. John Paul II called this the "law of self-giving."

Jesus expresses this point in John 12:25: "He who loves his life loses it, and he who hates his life in this world will keep it for eternal life." What are some ways you have experienced this truth (perhaps in your marriage or family, with some act of service, or with God)?

_____

_____

_____

_____

_____

_____

_____

_____

_____

_____

_____

_____

_____

_____

_____

Closing Prayer

(5 minutes)

For our closing prayer, let us ask Jesus, the Good Shepherd who lays down his life for his sheep, to guide us to walk in his ways, so that we may imitate his perfect, self-giving love. We will do this by praying or singing the traditional hymn, "The King of Love My Shepherd Is" by Henry W. Baker, 1868.

The King of love my Shepherd is,
whose goodness faileth never:
I nothing lack if I am his
and he is mine forever.

Where streams of living water flow
my ransomed soul he leadeth
and, where the verdant pastures grow,
with food celestial feedeth.

Perverse and foolish oft I strayed,
but yet in love he sought me
and on his shoulder gently laid
and home rejoicing brought me.

In death's dark vale I fear no ill
with thee, dear Lord, beside me;
thy rod and staff my comfort still,
thy cross before to guide me.

Thou spred'st a table in my sight;
thine unction grace bestoweth;
and, oh, what transport of delight
from thy pure chalice floweth!

And so through all the length of days
thy goodness faileth never;
Good Shepherd, may I sing thy praise
within thy house forever.

Step 4: Home Preparation – Looking Ahead

Read **John 13–17** and the **Session Seven Overview** on page 72. In this "farewell discourse" at the Last Supper, Jesus gives a New Commandment in John 13:34: "Love one another … as I have loved you." What do you think it means to love one another *as Jesus loves us?* How do we see Jesus' love for us in his teachings and in his actions in this Last Supper with his apostles?

_____

_____

_____

_____

_____

_____

_____

_____

The Last Supper, by Marten de Vos

Session Seven

The New Commandment and Life in the Spirit

John 13–17

Session Overview

Icon of Christ as the True Vine, Anonymous

Some of the apostles feel overwhelmed by the New Commandment Jesus gives in John 13:34: "Love one another ... as I have loved you." Even though we have sinned, Jesus loves us perfectly—totally, completely, and unconditionally, not expecting anything back. How can we possibly love our neighbor as Jesus has so perfectly loved us?

On our own, such a high standard of love would be impossible for us fallen sinners. But in today's session, we will see how Jesus promises to send his Holy Spirit, the Counselor, who will help us to do what we cannot do on our own. Jesus says the Spirit will dwell within us and help us remember Christ's teachings and bear witness to him. Most of all, the Spirit will take what belongs to Jesus and proclaim it to us. Let's now consider how that life in the Holy Spirit can transform our weak, fallen hearts and enable us to love one another with Christ's love radiating through us.

Step 1: Opening Review (5 minutes)

- In the last session, we discussed the law of self-giving summed up in John 12:25: "He who loves his life loses it, and he who hates his life in this world, will keep it for eternal life." What is the meaning of this law of self-giving?

  We gain when we give to others. We don't lose anything but gain happiness closeness to God

- How did Jesus exemplify this kind of self-giving love as the Good Shepherd?

  He gave his life for his flock (us)

Now, in this session, we will look at the New Commandment Jesus gives his followers as well as the gift of the Holy Spirit, who will help us to follow this commandment.

Radiating Christ

Blessed John Henry Newman's prayer, "Radiating Christ," expresses well the spiritual themes in Jesus' "farewell discourse," especially his call for us to abide in him.

Dear Jesus, help me to spread your fragrance everywhere I go.
Flood my soul with your spirit and life.
Penetrate and possess my whole being, so utterly,
that my life may only be a radiance of yours.
Shine through me, and be so in me,
that every soul I come in contact with
may feel your presence in my soul.
Let them look up and see no longer me, but only Jesus!
Stay with me, and then I shall begin to shine as you shine;
so to shine as to be a light to others.
The light, O Jesus, will be all from you; none of it will be mine.
It will be you, shining on others through me.
Let me thus praise you the way you love best by shining on those around me.
Let me preach you without preaching, not by words but by my example,
by the catching force of the sympathetic influence of what I do,
the evident fullness of the love my heart bears to you. Amen

Step 2: Video Presentation (30-35 minutes)

The New Commandment and Life in the Spirit (John 13–17)

I. **New Commandment = Love One Another as I Have Loved You (12:34)**

    A. Reflections of the saints

    B. Jesus shows us how to live it out through his example

II. **Last Supper**

    A. Jesus knows "his hour has come" (13:1-4)

    B. Jesus washes the apostles' feet

        1. Common ritual in ancient Near Eastern cultures

            a. Arid climates

            b. Hygiene and hospitality issue

        2. Duty to wash feet usually fell to a household servant

            a. There is no servant at the Last Supper, so who should wash the disciples' feet?

            b. In rabbinic tradition, washing feet is a task unworthy even for a disciple

        3. Jesus, the Master, does this menial task out of love

            a. Shows great humility

            b. Humbles the apostles, who think themselves above such a task

4. Peter's response: He refuses to let Jesus wash his feet at first

5. Jesus' response

III. Challenge of Self-Giving Love

A. Is it even possible?

B. Reflections of the saints

1. St. Thérèse of Lisieux

   a. Overwhelmed by the New Commandment – how could I do this?

   b. One must love others as Jesus loved them

   c. Jesus does not command the impossible

   d. He loves others through us

2. St. Catherine of Siena

   a. How do I love God the way he loves me?

   b. By loving my neighbor

IV. Gift of the Holy Spirit

13. 27

A. Pentecost

1. Descent of the Holy Spirit upon the apostles

2. Contrast apostles' behavior

   a. Fear after Good Friday, in hiding

    b. Bold preaching of Christ after the coming of the Holy Spirit

    c. They have an amazing transformation

  3. Bold proclamation of the gospel in Jerusalem, baptizing three thousand people in one day

  4. Ask for the help of the Holy Spirit in areas where we need to grow

B. Working of the Spirit

  1. The Spirit dwells with us and is in us – "I will pray to the Father, and he will give you another Counselor, to be with you for ever" (14:16)

  2. Helps us to be witnesses to Christ – "But when the Counselor comes, whom I shall send to you from the Father, even the Spirit of truth, who proceeds from the Father, he will bear witness to me" (15:26)

  3. Guides us in the truth (see 16:13)

  4. "He will glorify me ... All that the Father has is mine; therefore I said that he will take what is mine and declare it to you" (16:14-15)

    a. We are given what is Jesus' through the Holy Spirit

    b. Makes us children of God by grace

  5. Infuses us with sanctifying grace = God's very life dwelling within us

  6. Power of the Holy Spirit in our lives

    a. Image of an iron rod placed in a furnace

    b. Becomes red hot, transformed by the fire

    c. Our nature is transformed in the furnace of the Holy Spirit

    d. Able to love as he loves

C. Other effects of the Holy Spirit in the "farewell discourse"

    1. Christ is the vine, we are the branches (see John 15:5)

        a. Not just an external help

        b. Jesus abides in us through the Spirit, changing us from the inside out

    2. Unity

        a. As brothers and sisters in Christ, we become one

        b. Image of the unity between the Father and Son (see 17:21)

        c. One, holy, catholic, and apostolic Church = unity of faith, worship, and authority in the successors of the apostles

    3. Participation in Christ's passion

        a. "You will weep and lament, but the world will rejoice … your sorrow will turn into joy" (16:20)

        b. A woman in labor no longer remembers the pain after the birth of a child

        c. "No one will take your joy from you" (16:22)

– Takeaways –

1. "Love one another … as I have loved you."

2. Jesus sends the Holy Spirit to help us love as he loves.

Step 3: Small-Group Fellowship (30-40 minutes)
Discussion Questions

1. According to the video presentation, what was so shocking about Jesus washing the disciples' feet?

This was a menial task not one a Rabbi would do

2. It is at the Last Supper that Judas leaves to go betray Jesus. Even though Jesus knows what Judas is going to do, he still washes Judas' feet and gives him the Eucharist. How does his example challenge us to love those who frustrate us, disappoint us, or even hurt us?

Love your enemy; Be kind and treat them all w/ patience + kindness.

3. Why have the saints, like St. Thérèse of Lisieux, felt so overwhelmed by the New Commandment Jesus gave: "Love one another … as I have loved you"? Read **John 13:34.**

_____

_____

_____

_____

_____

_____

_____

_____

_____

_____

_____

_____

4. How are we fallen, weak human beings capable of living out this New Commandment? How can we possibly love our neighbor as Jesus, the divine Son of God, has so perfectly loved us?

_____

_____

_____

_____

_____

5. At the Last Supper, Jesus promises to send his Spirit, the Counselor. What is the effect of the Holy Spirit coming upon the apostles at Pentecost? How are they changed by the Holy Spirit?

_____

_____

_____

_____

_____

_____

_____

_____

_____

_____

6. Read **John 14:16-17, 15:26-27, and 16:13-15.** How might the same Holy Spirit help us in our daily struggles?

_____

_____

_____

_____

_____

_____

_____

_____

_____

7. Jesus prays to the Father for all Christians throughout the generations, "that they may all be one; even as thou, Father, art in me, and I in thee" (John 17:21). What kind of unity does Jesus want Christians to have? What does this tell us about the sad divisions in Christianity today?

_____

_____

_____

_____

_____

_____

_____

_____

_____

_____

_____

Pentecost, by Jean II Restout

Closing Prayer

(5 minutes)

For our closing prayer, let us pray or sing a few verses from the traditional hymn, "Come, Holy Ghost":

Come, Holy Ghost, Creator blest,
and in our souls take up thy rest;
come with thy grace and heavenly aid
to fill the hearts which thou hast made;

O Comforter, to thee we cry,
O heavenly gift of God Most High,
O fount of life and fire of love,
and sweet anointing from above.

Kindle our senses from above,
and make our hearts overflow with love;
with patience firm and virtue high
the weakness of our flesh supply.

Oh, may thy grace on us bestow
the Father and the Son to know;
and thee, through endless times confessed,
of both the eternal Spirit blest.

Now to the Father and the Son,
Who rose from death, be glory given,
with thou, O holy Comforter, henceforth by all
in earth and heaven. Amen.

Step 4: Home Preparation – Looking Ahead

Read **John 18–21** and the **Session Eight Overview** on page 84. As you read the Passion narrative in John's Gospel, consider the ways the following people respond to Jesus in his moment of great suffering: Peter, the chief priests, Pilate, the Beloved Disciple, Mary, and Nicodemus.

_____

_____

_____

_____

_____

_____

_____

_____

_____

Christ's Appearance to Mary Magdalene after the Resurrection, by Alexander Ivanov

"It Is Finished": A Dying and Rising Love

John 18–21

Session Overview

Christ on the Cross, by Carl Heinrich Bloch

The Passion narrative in John's Gospel underscores that Jesus is not going to his death as a passive victim. From beginning to end, Jesus is the one in charge of the situation. In the Garden of Gethsemane, where he is arrested, Jesus knows Judas, his betrayer, is coming. He goes out to meet the soldiers who are going to take him away. Though he is the Son of God and could call upon his angels to rescue him, Jesus voluntarily surrenders himself and goes on trial before the chief priests and then before Pilate.

Several times, Jesus is mocked for claiming to be King. Soldiers put a crown of thorns on his head, dress him in a purple robe (the color for royalty), and shout out, "Hail, King of the Jews." The soldiers mean it in jest, but John's Gospel records it to show how all these mocking actions point to a truth the soldiers do not realize: Jesus is the true King of Kings. His crucifixion is his enthronement. His death is his great victory.

John's Gospel also goes out of its way to show that when Jesus is on the Cross, several prophecies and Old Testament foreshadowings are fulfilled: The soldiers cast lots for Jesus' tunic, fulfilling the prophecy "for my raiment they cast lots" (Psalm 22:18). Jesus is crucified at the sixth hour, the hour when Passover lambs would have been sacrificed. And he dies without having his legs broken, like a Passover lamb whose legs were not supposed to be broken.

Step 1: Opening Review (5 minutes)

- In the last session, we discussed the Great Commandment and the gift of the Holy Spirit, which Jesus taught about at the Last Supper. What was that Great Commandment? And how does the Holy Spirit help us to live it out?

_____

_____

_____

_____

_____

_____

_____

_____

Now, let's turn our attention to the climax of the fourth Gospel: Jesus' passion, death, and resurrection.

Love: *Philia* or *Agapē*

Jesus twice asks Peter, "Do you love me *[agapas me]?*" In other words, "Do you love me, Peter, with this total, unconditional love?" Prior to his denying Christ, Peter undoubtedly would have said, "Yes, Lord, I do love you unconditionally *[agapō se]!*" But as Pope Benedict explained, "Now that he has known the bitter sadness of infidelity, the drama of his own weakness, he says with humility: 'Lord; you know that I love you *[philō se],*' that is, 'I love you with my poor human love.'"[1]

Jesus asks Peter a third time if he loves him, but this time, he speaks only of the poor, human love that Peter can give. "Do you love me *[phileis me]?*" "Simon understands that his poor love is enough for Jesus, it is the only one of which he is capable … He thus replies, 'Lord, you know everything; you know that I love you *[philō se].*' This is to say that Jesus has put himself on the level of Peter, rather than Peter on Jesus' level!"[2]

---

[1] Pope Benedict XVI, *The Apostles* (San Francisco: Ignatius, 207), 47.
[2] Ibid, 47-48.

Step 2: Video Presentation (30-35 minutes)

"It Is Finished": A Dying and Rising Love (John 18–21)

I. Passion Narrative

    A. Betrayal in the Garden of Gethsemane (18:1-11)

        1. Jesus is in control of the situation

            a. He understands what is happening – and what will happen

            b. He willingly allows himself to be taken away

            c. He goes forward and seeks out the soldiers

        2. "Whom do you seek?" (18:4)

            a. "I AM" *[egō eimi]* – uses divine Name

            b. Soldiers fall to the ground at the power of Jesus' words

    B. Trial before the Sanhedrin (18:12-24)

        1. Sanhedrin = council of Jewish leaders: Sadducees and Pharisees

        2. Sadducees

            a. Chief priests, stewards/guardians of the Temple

            b. Had strong resistance to Jesus' message

            c. Concerned Romans would intervene and take away their authority

        3. Pharisees

            a. Guardians of the *Torah*

            b. Influential movement

            c. Respected by people for living out the *Torah* with great rigor

4. Jesus seemingly violated the Law, particularly regarding the Sabbath

5. Caiaphas, high priest on the council

   a. Cannot execute Jesus due to Roman law

   b. Sends Jesus to Pilate to get Rome to condemn him

C. Trial before Pilate (see 18:28–19:16)

   1. Jewish leaders accuse Jesus of being a threat to Roman authority

   2. Pilate sees that Jesus is not a criminal, but was handed over by the Sanhedrin out of envy

   3. Pilate's cowardice

      a. Fear of the crowds and rioting

      b. Fear of Caesar's response

      c. Knows Jesus is innocent but hands him over anyway

   4. "What is truth?" (18:38)

      a. Rhetorical question – Pilate does not really care about the truth

      b. In today's relativistic culture, everyone has own "truth"

      c. Will we stand up with Jesus for the truth?

   5. Jesus is scourged

D. Jesus' crucifixion, death, and burial (see 19:17-42)

   1. Crucifixion was not just a method of execution; it was designed to humiliate and discourage rebellion against Rome

   2. The Cross was not a moment of defeat but of triumph = Jesus' throne

   3. Royal symbolism

      a. Crown of thorns

      b. Purple robe

    c. Sign on the Cross: "Jesus of Nazareth, King of the Jews"

    d. One hundred pounds of myrrh and aloes used in Jesus' burial

  4. Fulfillments of Old Testament prophecies

    a. Psalm 22 – casting of lots for Jesus' garments

    b. Psalm 69:21 – "For my thirst they gave me vinegar to drink"

    c. Zechariah 12:10 – They shall "look on him whom they have pierced"

  5. Jesus dies as Passover Lamb

    a. Offers his life as sacrifice for humanity

    b. Crucified at the sixth hour, when the Passover lambs were sacrificed

    c. Hyssop branch – used in Egypt to put the blood on the doors (lintels) during the first Passover

    d. Passover lamb must be unblemished, legs unbroken (see Exodus 12:46)

II. Resurrection Accounts

  A. Mary Magdalene (see 20:1-18)

    1. Does not recognize Jesus at first, thinks he is a gardener

    2. She recognizes him when he calls her name

    3. "My sheep hear my voice, and I know them, and they follow me" (10:27)

  B. Apostles (see 20:19-25)

    1. Jesus' first words when he appears to them = "Peace be with you"

    2. Shows them his hands and side

    3. The apostles are frightened and in hiding when Jesus appears

4. All had fled on Good Friday, so they are fearful at his appearance

5. Words to Mary Magdalene: "Go to my brethren and tell them ..." (20:17, NAB)

   a. The apostles are still his brothers, despite their cowardice

   b. Jesus comes with mercy and peace

6. Jesus breathes on the apostles (see 20:21-23), gives them the power to forgive sins

C. Dialogue between Jesus and Peter (see 21:15-17)

1. Jesus asks Peter (calling him Simon) if he loves him

   a. In original Greek, Jesus says "Do you love *[agapō]* me more than these?"

   b. Peter responds: "Yes, Lord, I love *[philō]* you"

   c. *Agapē* = divine, sacrificial, total self-giving love

   d. *Philia* = human, friendship love

2. Third time, Jesus changes the verb for love, using *philō*

   a. Meets Peter where he is

   b. Someday, Peter will indeed love *[agapō]* truly by dying as a martyr

3. Our love can be transformed through our faith in Jesus

– *Takeaways* –

1. Jesus freely and lovingly offered himself on the Cross for us, for the forgiveness of our sins.

2. God accepts our imperfect love for him and empowers us to love him more perfectly.

Step 3: Small-Group Fellowship (30-40 minutes)

Discussion Questions

1. Read **John 18:1-11,** John's account of Jesus' arrest in the Garden of Gethsemane. How does John's Gospel highlight that Jesus is not a passive victim, but the one in control of the situation—willingly handing himself over, not taken away by force?

Meets the soldiers
acknowledges —
tells them who he is

2. On Good Friday, many people treat Jesus with royal honor, but only to mock him. John's Gospel highlights these instances to show how ironic their actions are: Jesus really is the true King. What are some ways we see Jesus treated with royalty in this mocking way in these scenes?

Crown of Thorns
"King of the Jews"
Purple Cloak

3. How is Jesus' death on Calvary presented as the sacrifice of the true Passover Lamb? Why is this parallel significant?

6th hour

hyssop branch

no broken legs

Mt. 27 v 25 –

Mk. 15 v 25 –

4. One of Jesus' last acts is to entrust his mother and the Beloved Disciple to each other in a special mother-son relationship. Read **John 19:26-27.** Why is this scene understood as Jesus entrusting Mary as the spiritual mother of all Christians?

5. On this first Easter, Jesus appears to Mary Magdalene and then to the apostles later in the evening. What is the significance of Jesus showing the apostles his hands and side and saying, "Peace be with you" (John 20:19), as his opening words to them?

_____

_____

_____

_____

_____

_____

6. On this same Easter evening, Jesus breathes the Holy Spirit on the apostles and gives them the authority to forgive sins. Consider Jesus' words: "As the Father has sent me, even so I send you" (John 20:21). Why did God send the Son? And what does that tell us about the apostles' mission to forgive sins?

_____

_____

_____

_____

_____

7. What do Jesus' next words—"if you forgive the sins of any, they are forgiven" (John 20:23)—tell us about the sacrament of reconciliation (confession)?

_____

_____

_____

_____

_____

_____

8. Jesus asks Peter three times, "Do you love me?" But in this dialogue, John's Gospel uses two different Greek words for love: *agapē* and *philia.* What are the differences between these two words for love?

_____

_____

_____

_____

_____

9. What does this dialogue tell us about the kind of love Jesus wants from us? The kind of love Peter admits he is able to give? The kind of love Jesus is willing to accept from us?

_____

_____

_____

_____

_____

_____

10. Looking back over this study, which scene from the Gospel of John touched your heart the most? How might that scene help you encounter Jesus anew and open up new ways for Jesus to transform your *philia* love for him ever more into *agapē?*

_____

_____

_____

_____

_____

_____

Christ and Saint Peter at the Sea of Galilee, by Scarsellino

Closing Prayer

(5 minutes)

At the end of this last session, take a moment to think about one key insight you have gained from this study of John's Gospel—something that has inspired you to follow Jesus more closely as a disciple. Thank Jesus for that insight, and ask him to help you live it out so that this study may continue to bear fruit in your life moving forward.

_____

_____

_____

Step 4: Looking Ahead

"Follow me!" (John 21:22). This is one of the last things Jesus says in the Gospel of John. While he originally addressed these words to St. Peter, they are meant for each and every one of us. Take some time to reflect on these words. What do they mean to you? How can you live them out in your own life? Now that you have spent time meeting Jesus in the Gospel of John, you can continue to encounter him in Scripture, daily prayer, and the Mass and by going to confession and loving and serving the people God has placed in your life.

_____

_____

_____

_____

_____

_____

_____

_____

_____

_____

_____

_____

_____

_____

_____

_____

_____

A Grand Expedition **Through the Bible**

Ready to explore the Bible in depth?

Continue with a **detailed** or **concise overview** of salvation history

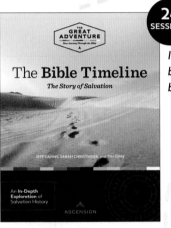

24 SESSIONS

In-depth study of the biblical story from beginning to end

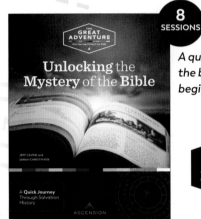

8 SESSIONS

A quick journey through the biblical story from beginning to end

Or **continue the journey** with an in-depth book study

10 SESSIONS

11 SESSIONS

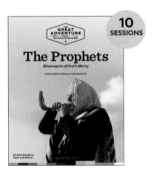

10 SESSIONS

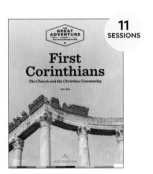

11 SESSIONS

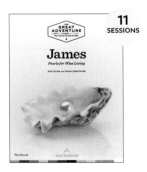

11 SESSIONS

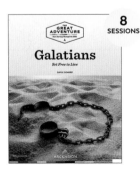

8 SESSIONS

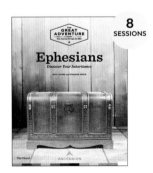

8 SESSIONS

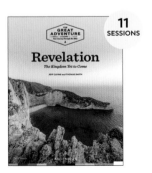

11 SESSIONS

The Heart of the Catholic Faith

Want a deeper understanding of the foundations of Catholicism ?

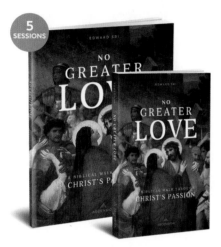

5 SESSIONS

No Greater Love

Walk with Jesus from the Garden of Gethsemane to the Mount of Calvary. Come to a deeper understanding and appreciation of God's immeasurable and unconditional love—and draw closer to Jesus than ever before.

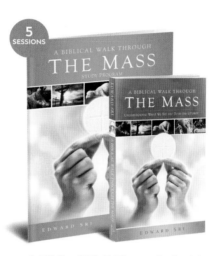

5 SESSIONS

A Biblical Walk Through the Mass

Explore the biblical roots of words and gestures throughout the Mass. Learn their profound significance and bring new life to your liturgical experience.

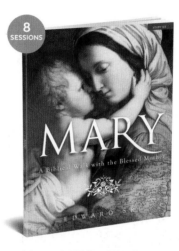

8 SESSIONS

Mary: A Biblical Walk With the Blessed Mother

Filmed on location in the Holy Land, this study takes you through Mary's joys and sorrows. Learn how she works in our lives, drawing us closer to Jesus.

8 SESSIONS

Oremus: A Guide to Catholic Prayer

This study guides you through simple yet profound steps to an effective and fruitful prayer life. Learn how to express yourself to God in prayer, and how to hear his voice—even in the smallest encounters of daily life.

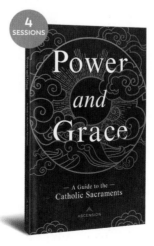

4 SESSIONS

Power and Grace: A Guide to the Catholic Sacraments

A quick introduction to the seven Catholic sacraments, *Power and Grace* features material curated from our popular sacramental preparation and teen programs such as *Chosen*, *Altaration*, and *Belonging*.

Wisdom **for Life**

Interested in applying your faith to everyday life?

The Activated Disciple: Taking Your Faith to the Next Level

Transform every area of your life to become more like Christ. Move beyond believing and practicing your faith, and begin radically living it.

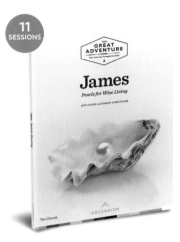

James: Pearls for Wise Living

For anyone who struggles to live a truly Christian life, *James* offers a wealth of practical solutions for handling and even sanctifying everyday circumstances.

Follow Me: Meeting Jesus in the Gospel of John

Jesus wants you to be more than just a believer—he wants you to be his disciple. In *Follow Me*, experience the joy of a renewed friendship with Christ.

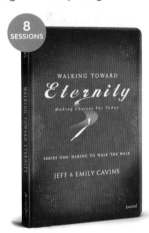

Walking Toward Eternity: Daring to Walk the Walk

This program introduces seven key virtues and outlines practical steps for living them out in daily life. Be drawn into a life-changing encounter with Christ through *lectio divina*.

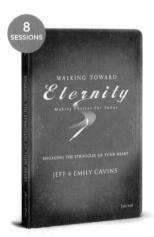

Walking Toward Eternity: Engaging the Struggles of Your Heart

This practical study offers insights into common obstacles, such as greed, envy, fear, and shame. Learn how to engage obstacles in your Christian walk in a positive way as you continue toward the goal of union with Christ.

Wisdom: God's Vision for Life

Learn new habits for increasing wisdom in your daily life. Gain confidence, through role models and practice, in living according to God's vision.

About the Author

Dr. Edward Sri is provost and professor of theology and Scripture at the Augustine Institute and founding leader, with Curtis Martin, of FOCUS (Fellowship of Catholic University Students). He is author and presenter of *A Biblical Walk Through the Mass* and *Mary: A Biblical Walk with the Blessed Mother*. He holds a doctorate from the Pontifical University of St. Thomas Aquinas in Rome.